CONNECT THE DOTS

Age-Proof Your Brain!

Puzzle Constructors: Keith Burns, Peter Grosshauser, Chuck Whelon, Alex Willmore

Illustrators: Chris Gattorna, Jen Torche

Cover Puzzle: Alex Willmore

ISBN-13: 978-1-4508-3109-3
ISBN-10: 1-4508-3109-5

Manufactured in USA.

8 7 6 5 4 3 2 1

Lab Rat

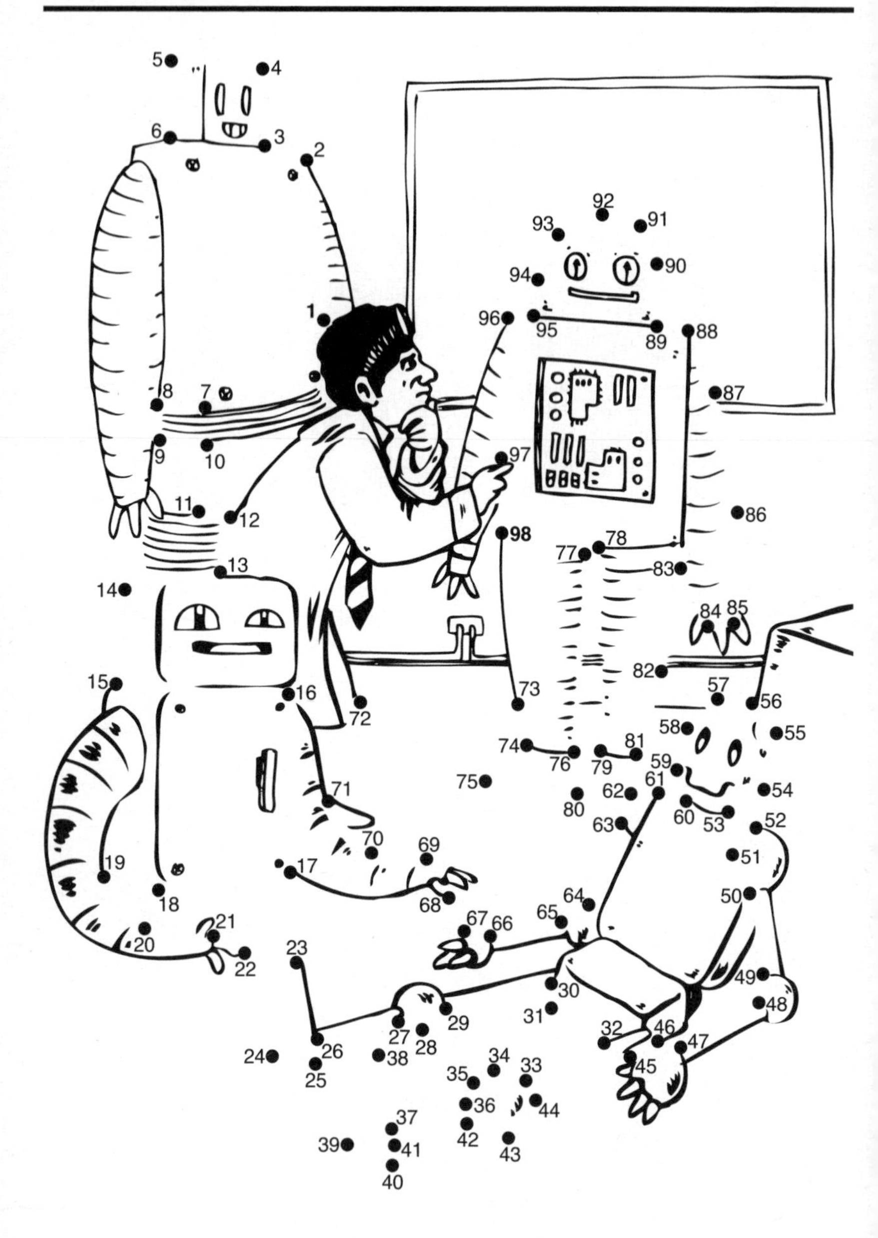

Arctic Animal

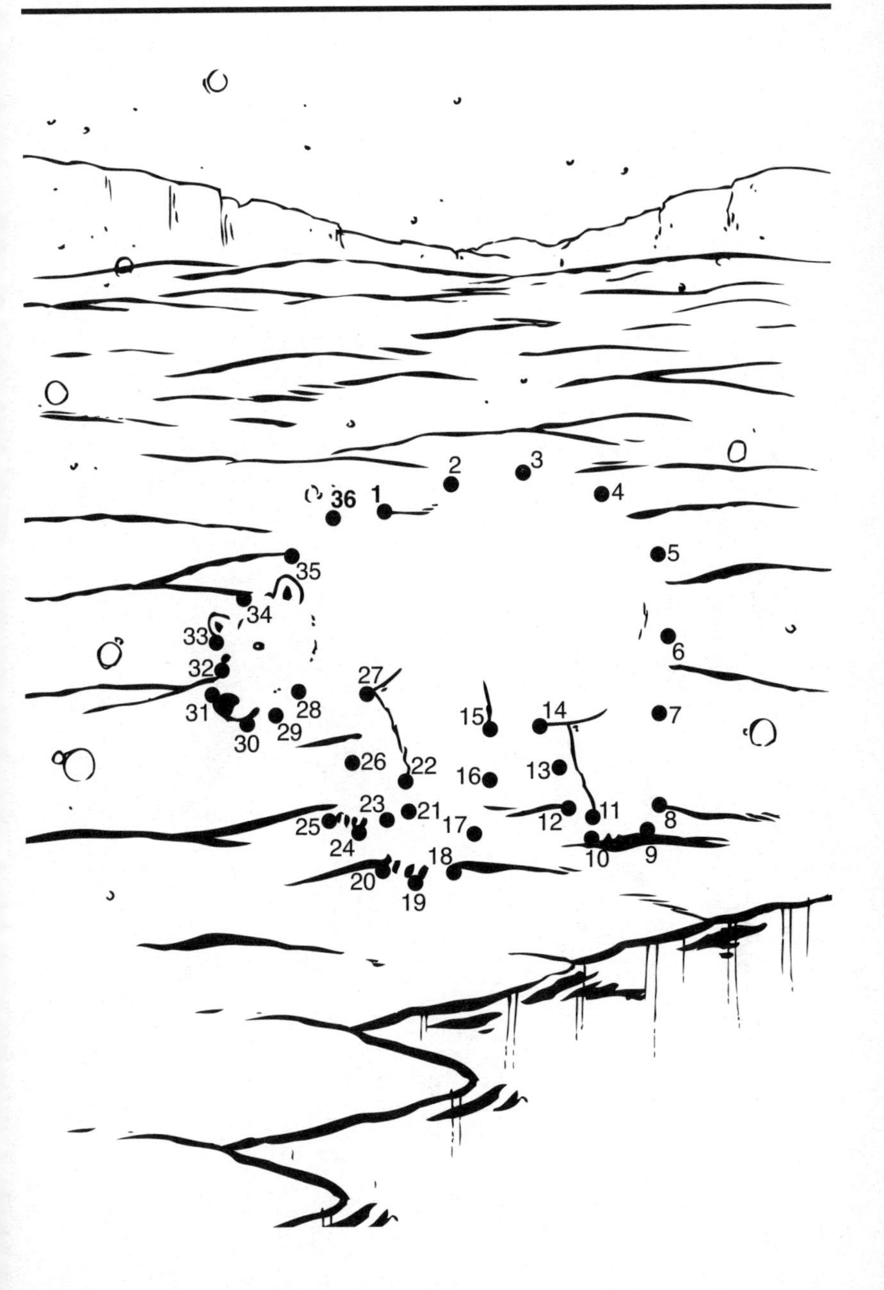

Batter Up

Harriet's Hip Hairdo

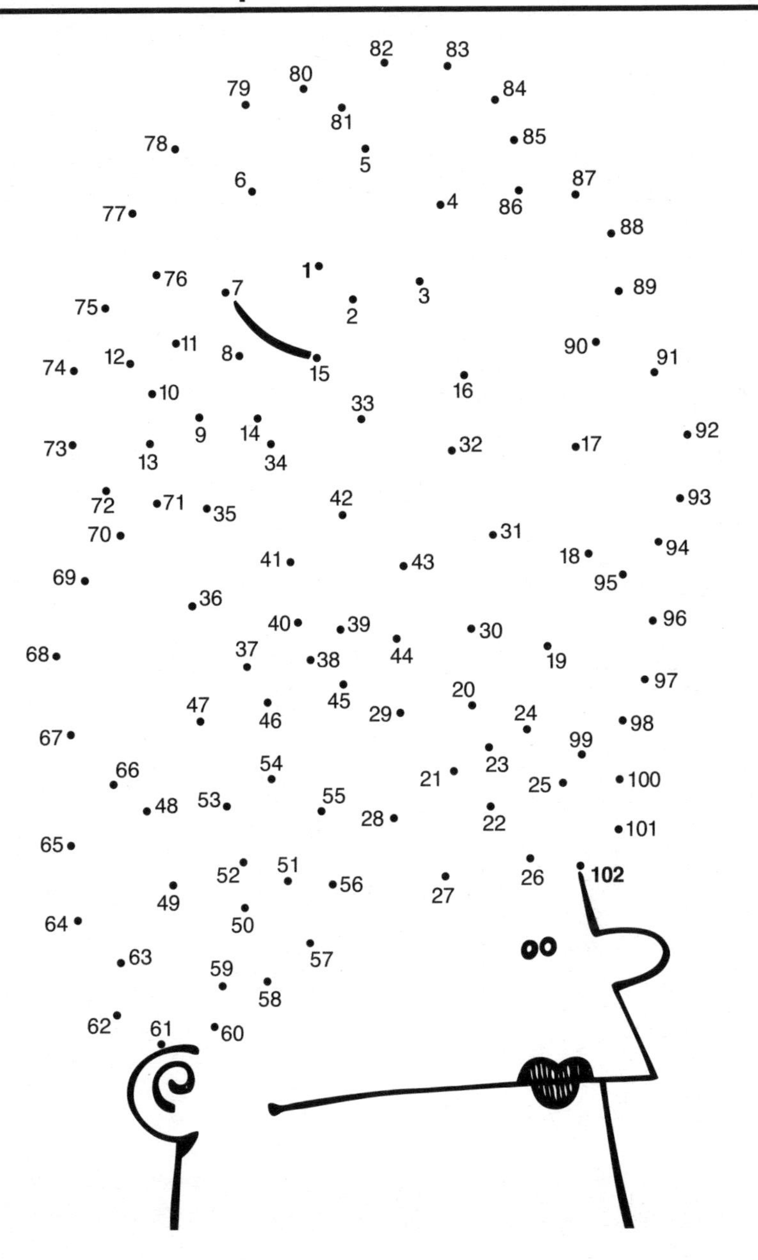

Under Water

Connect the numbers to reveal the aquarium decorations. Connect the letters to spell the names of the animals in the tank, clownfish, electric eel, terrapin, snail, and shark.

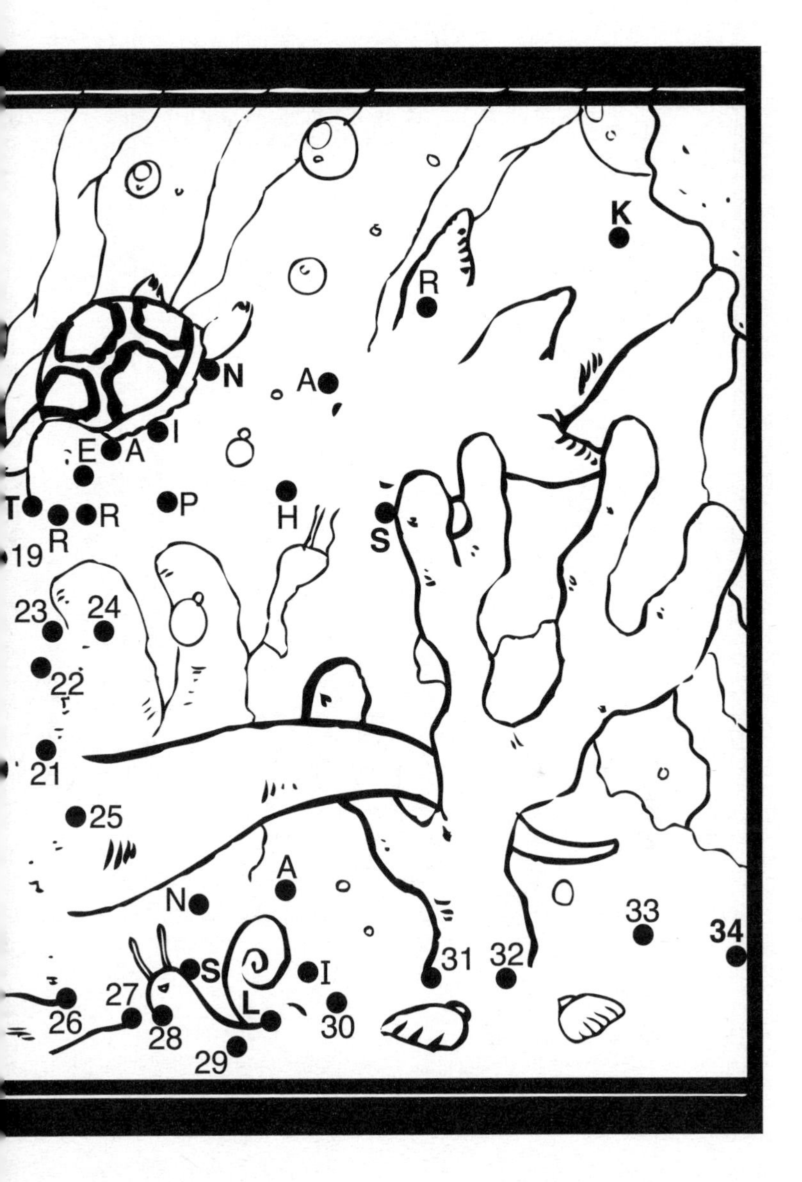
K
R
N
A
I
E
A
T
R
P
H
S
R
19
23
24
22
21
25
A
N
33
34
31
32
S
I
27
L
26
28
30
29

Crustacean Sensation

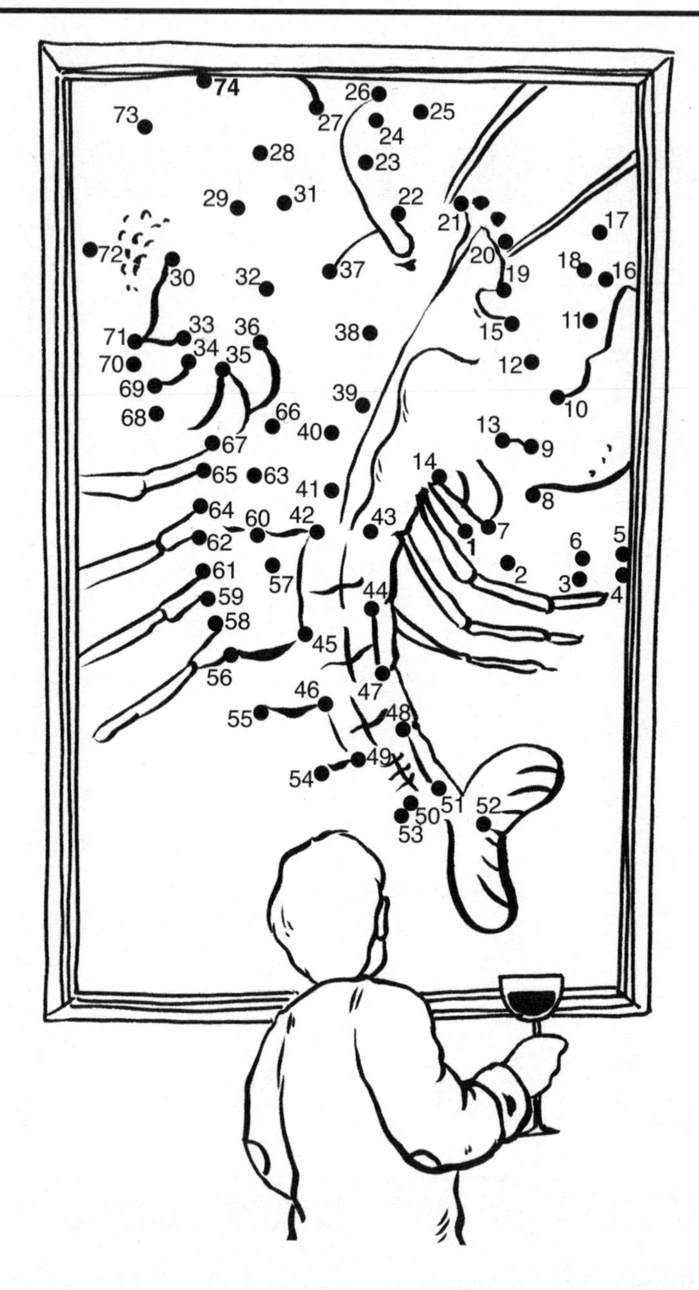

Close Encounter

What a Mess!

Undersea Surprise

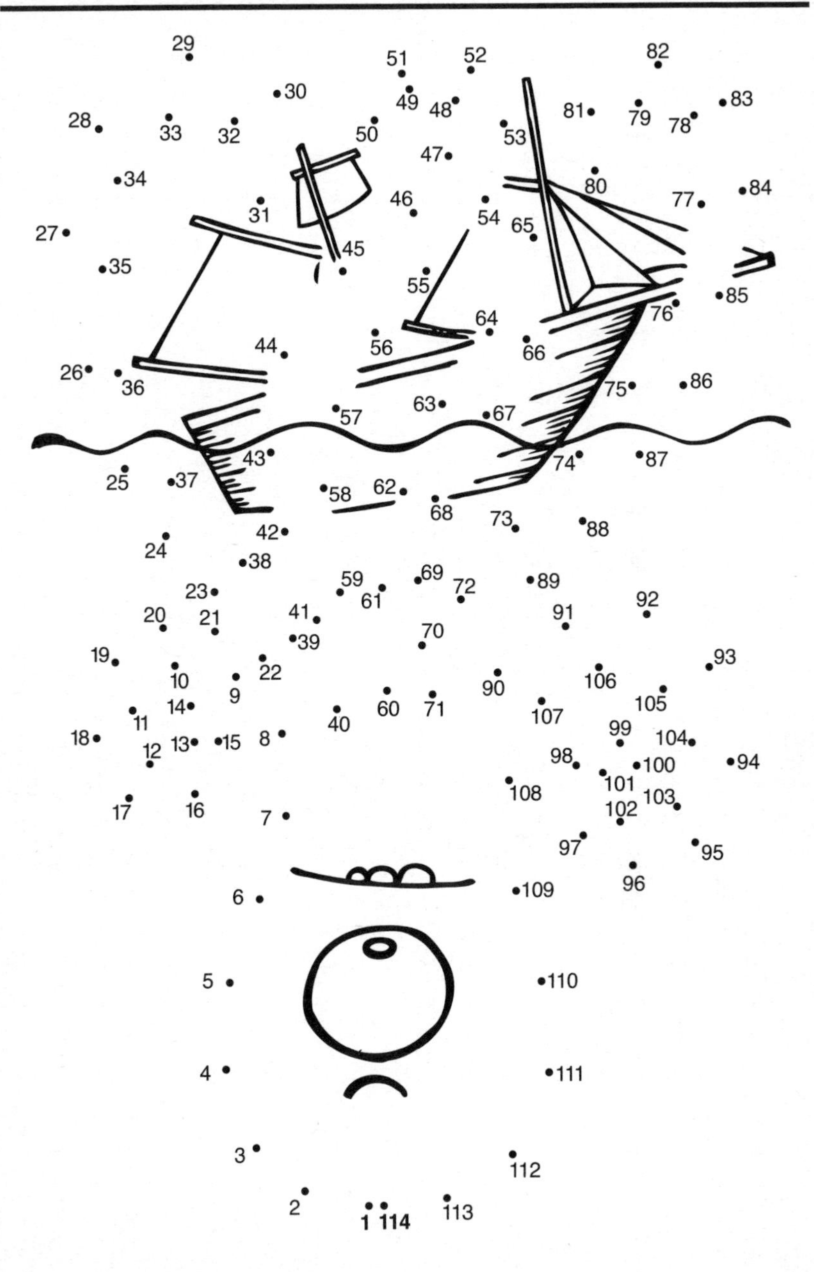

Island Rescue

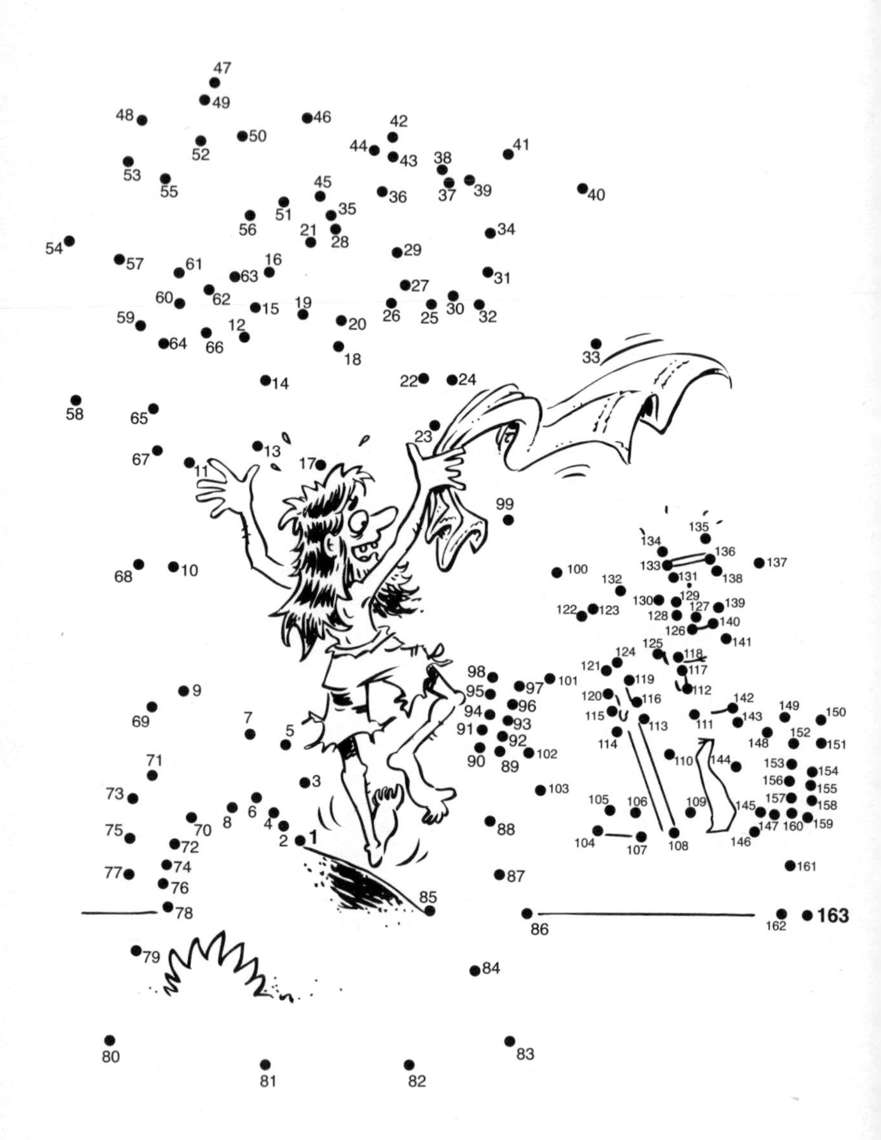

Catch of the Day

Jam Time

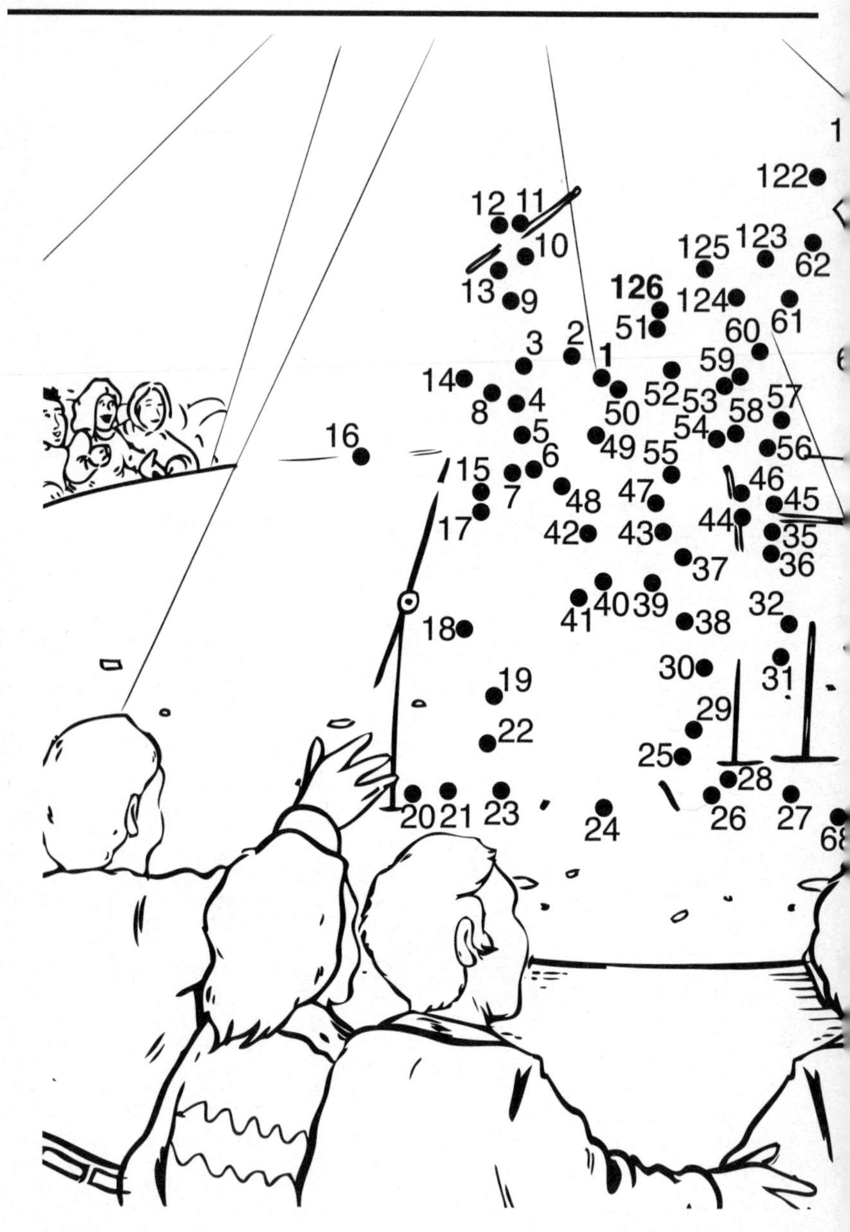

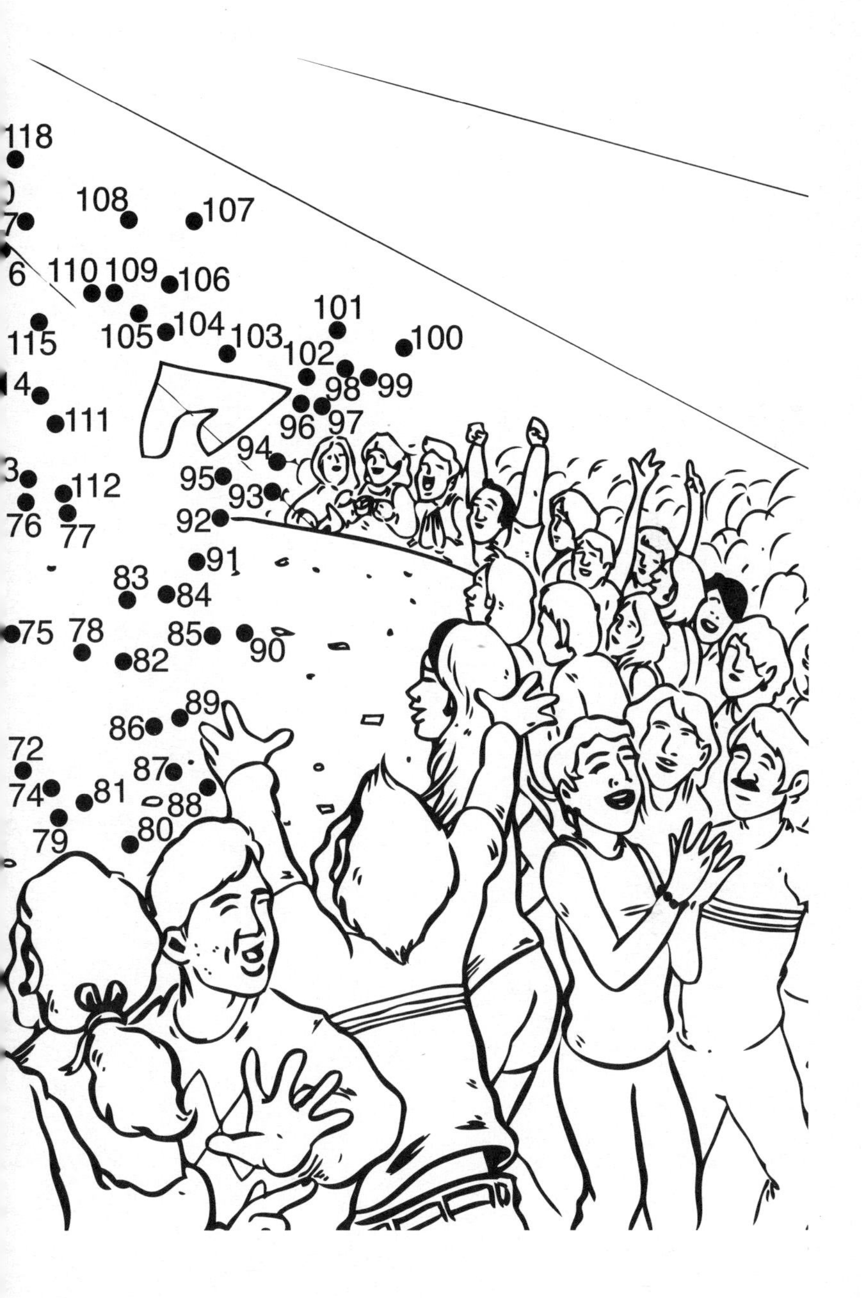
118
108
107
110
109
106
101
115
105
104
103
100
102
99
98
111
96
97
94
95
112
93
92
76
77
91
83
84
75
78
85
90
82
89
86
72
87
74
81
88
79
80

Bigfoot

Plunger Problems

Soaring Through the Skies

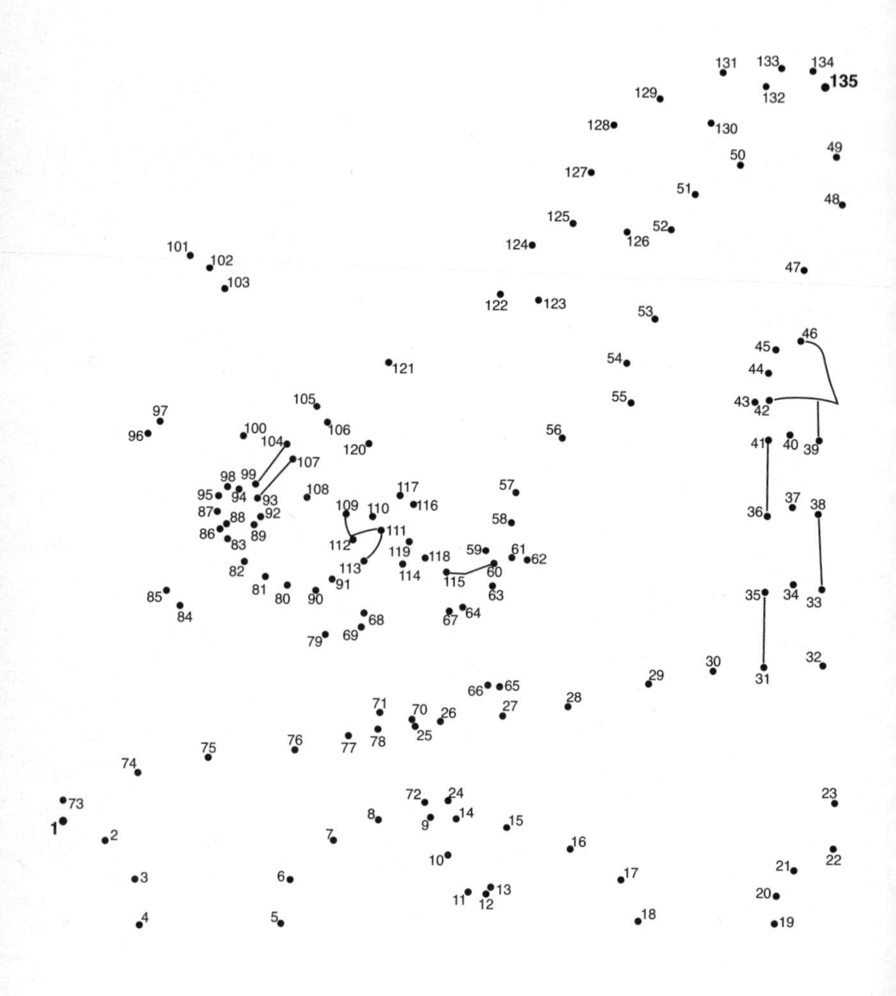

Mountains of Fun

Tub Time

Connect the letters and consecutive numbers, starting at A and ending at K, and starting at 1 and ending at 32, for a relaxing scene.

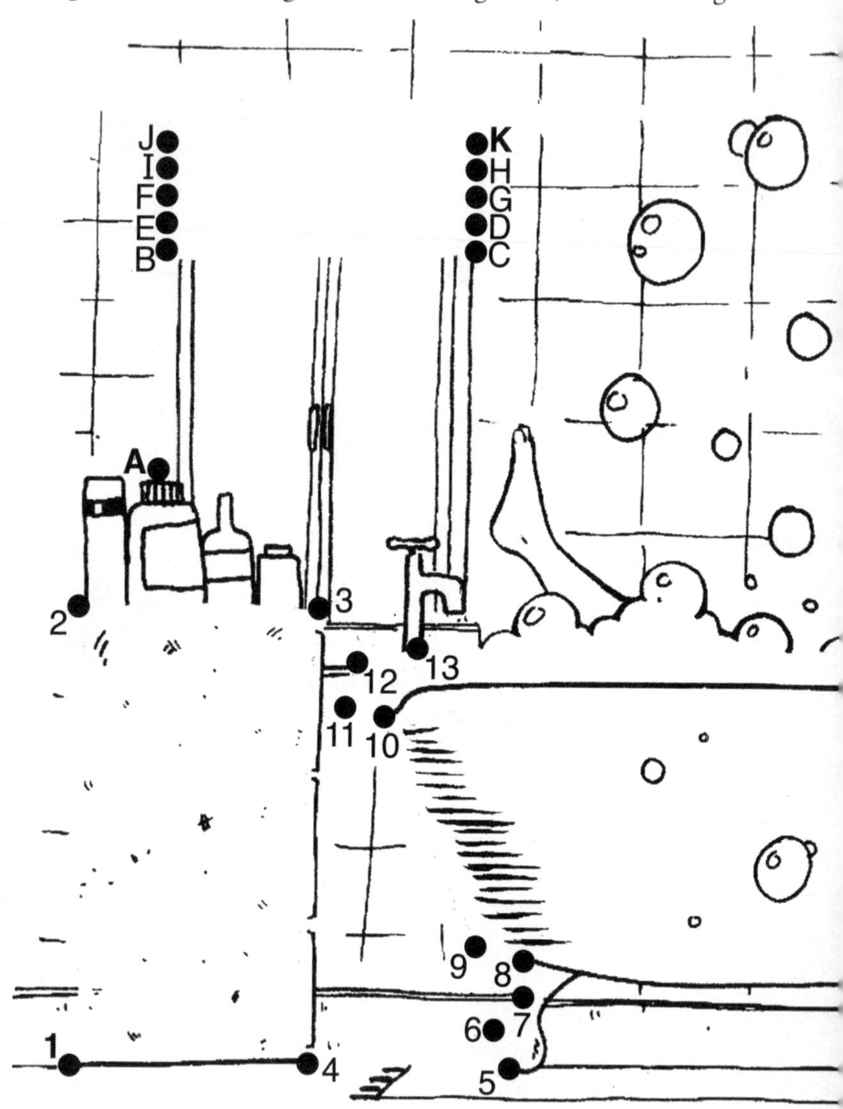

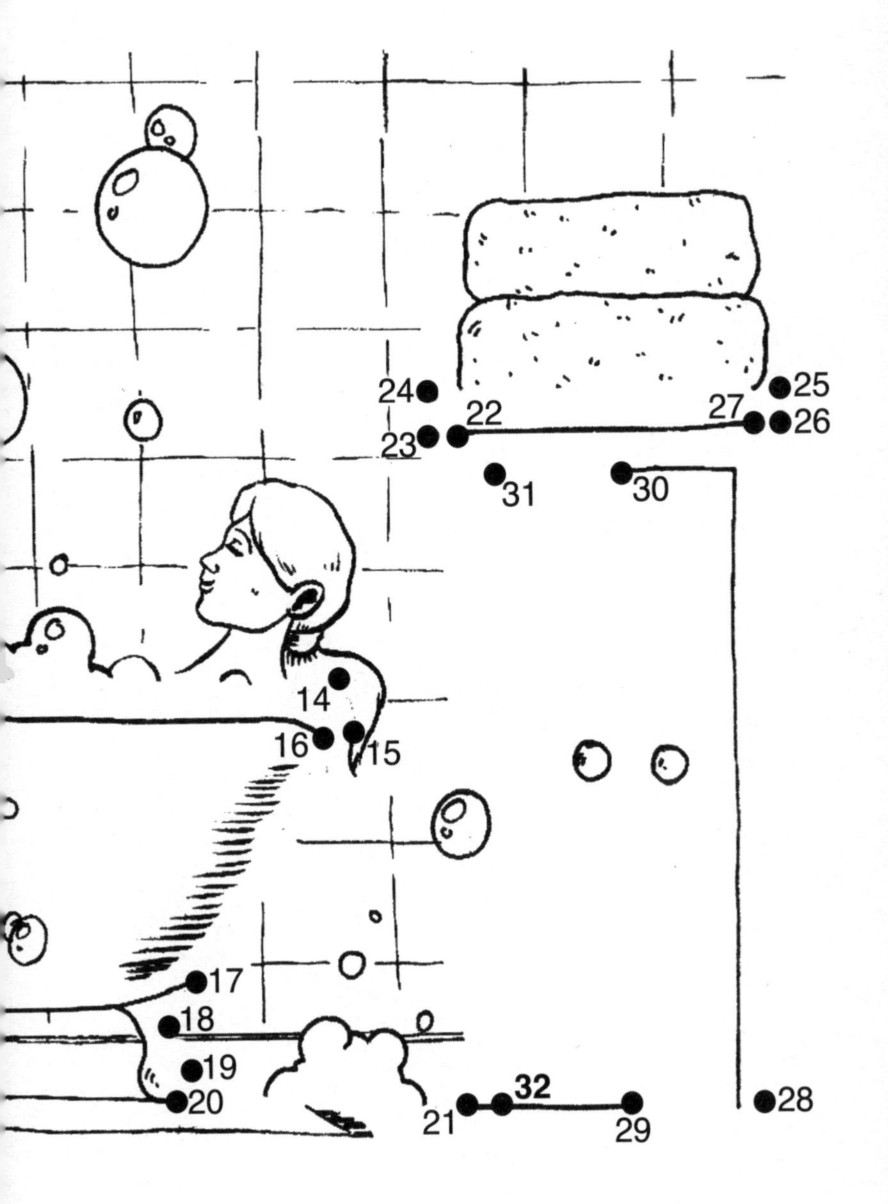
24
25
22
27
23
26
31
30
14
16
15
17
18
19
20
32
21
29
28

On Safari

Connect the letters to spell the names of each animal, African elephant, zebras, and sleeping lion.

Modern Windmills

Sailing, Sailing

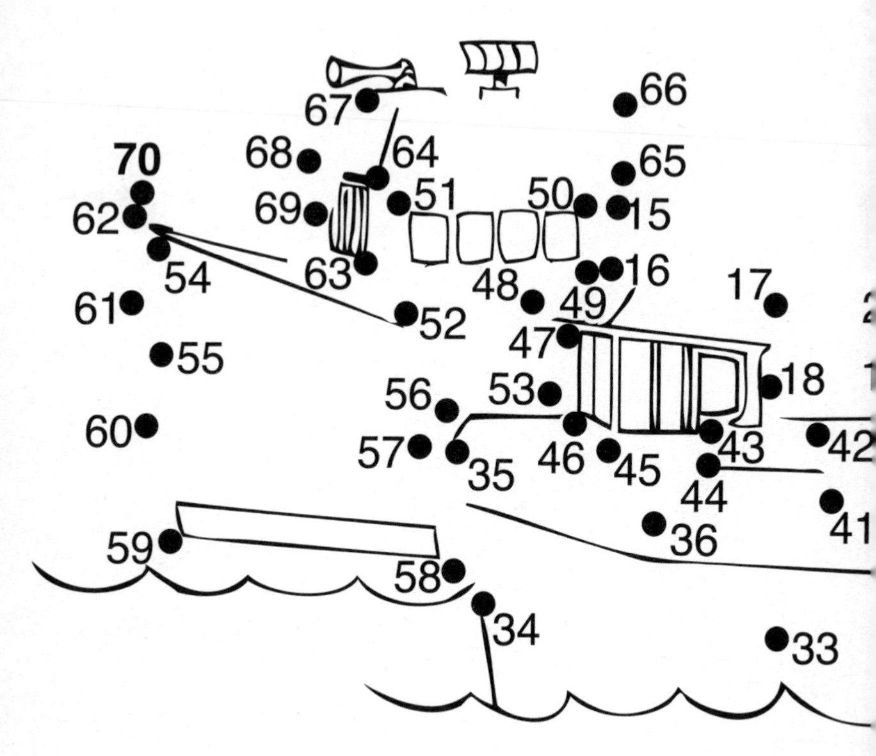

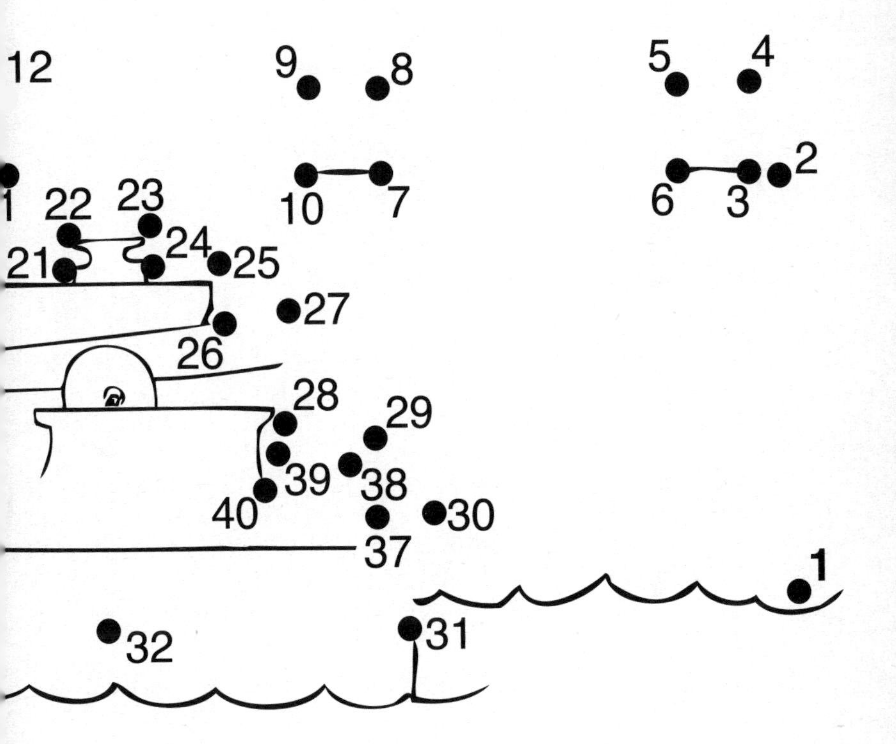

Astro Ape

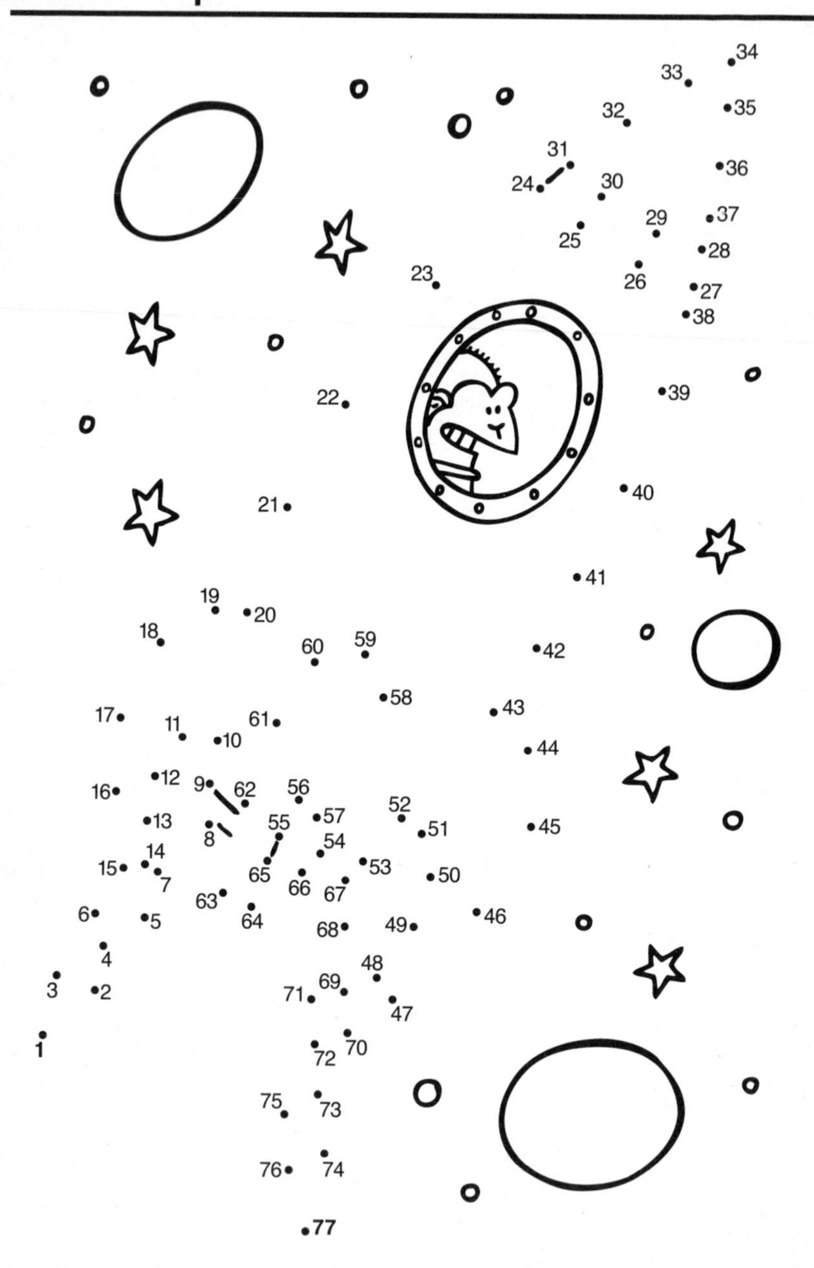

It's a Bird, It's a . . .

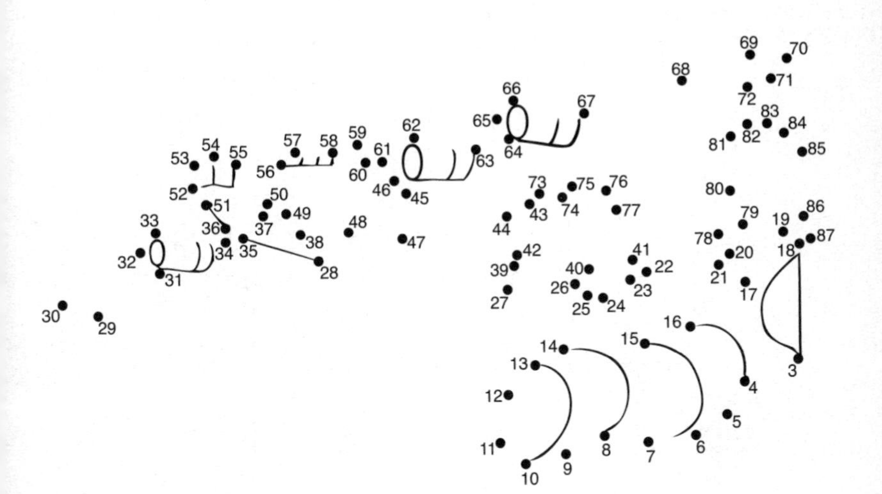

Riding the Rails

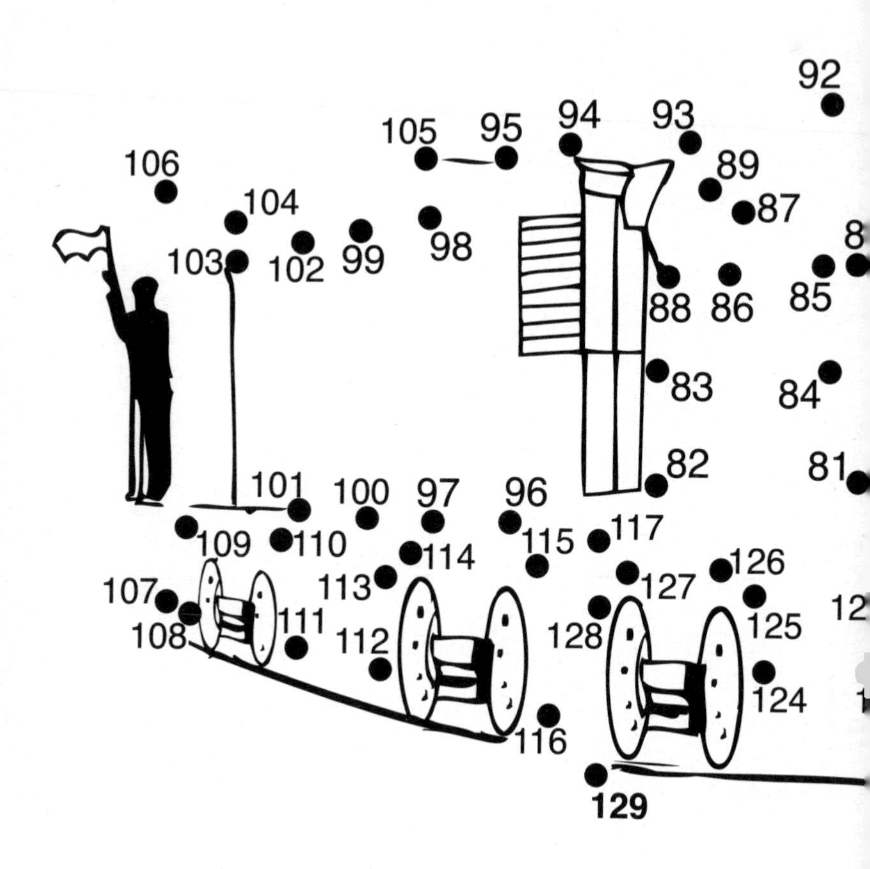

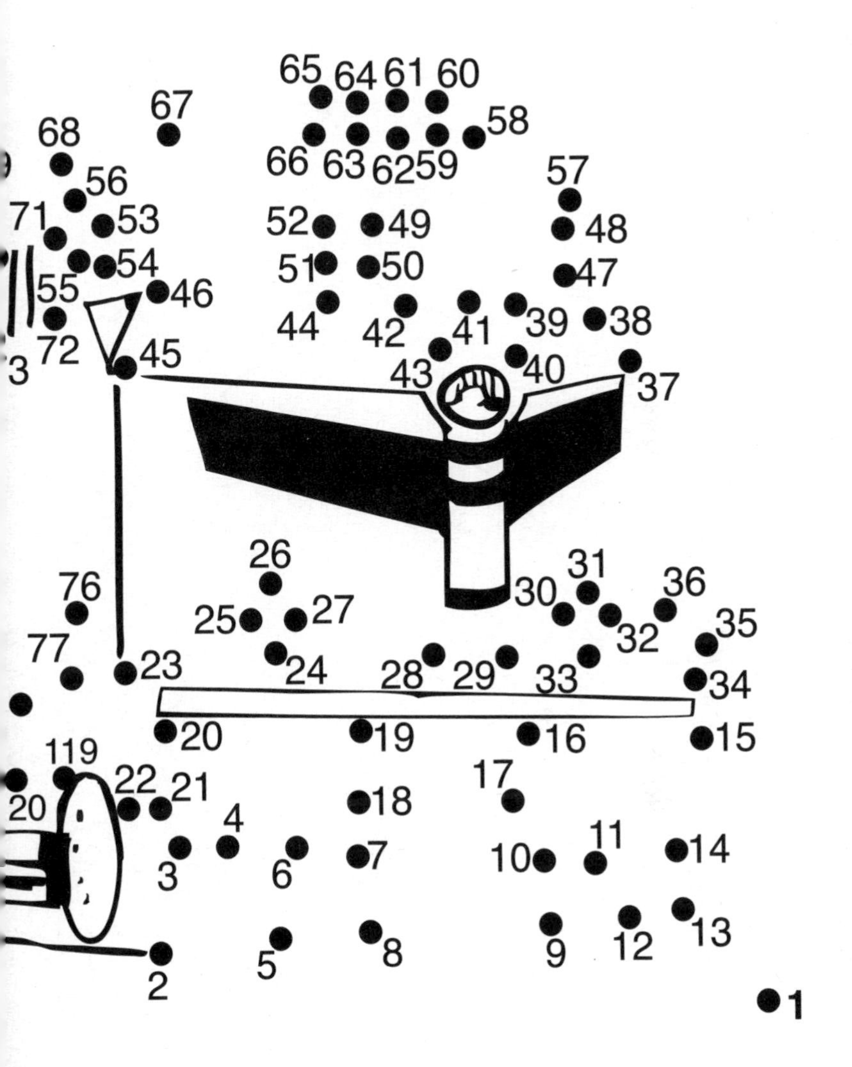

Monster on the Rampage!

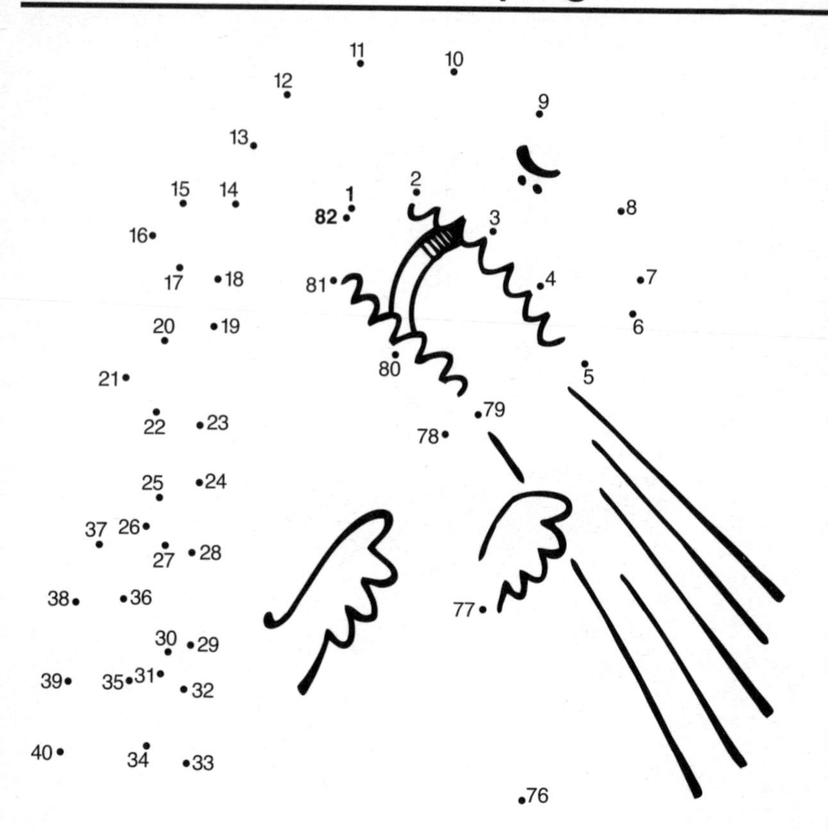

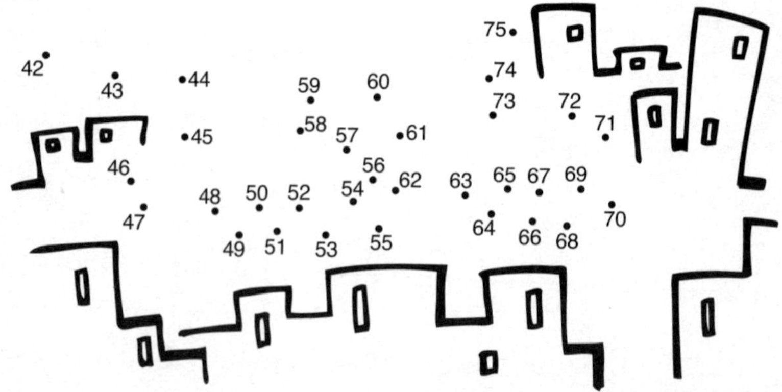

Robot

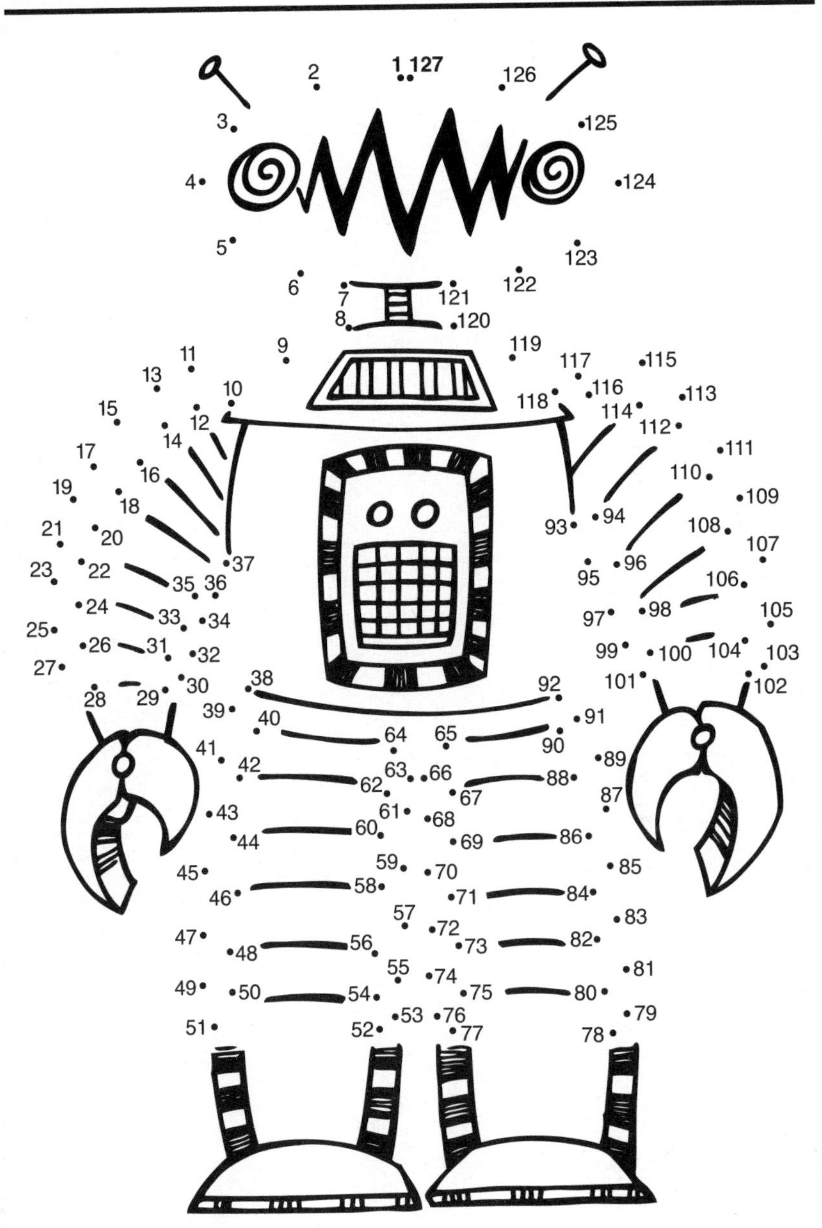

Truck Stop